Help with homework

Maths

revision

HI, MY NAME IS *KITCAT*...

... AND I'M *DIG*.

WE ARE HERE TO HELP YOU THROUGH THESE EXERCISES. START AT THE BEGINNING AND DON'T DO TOO MUCH IN ONE GO.

IT WON'T BE EASY ALL THE TIME – SOME PAGES CAN BE TRICKY – BUT WE'VE GIVEN YOU THE ANSWERS IN CASE YOU GET REALLY STUCK. NO PEEPING THOUGH! YOU WILL RECOGNISE A LOT OF THIS FROM THE WORK YOU DO AT SCHOOL (SORRY!). NOW YOU WISH YOU'D PAID MORE ATTENTION... *GOOD LUCK!*

Written by Nina Filipek
Designed and illustrated by Dan Green
Cover design by Dan Green

www.autumnchildrensbooks.co.uk

number values

Each digit in a number has a **value**.

For example:
3450 = 3000 + 400 + 50 + 0

Remember:
9999 = 9000 + 900 + 90 + 9

Write the missing number values in the boxes.

a. 4098 = ☐ + ☐ + 90 + ☐   **b.** 5667 5000 ☐ ☐ ☐

c. 3824 = ☐ + 800 + ☐ + ☐   **d.** 1951 = ☐ + ☐ + ☐ + 1

Find out:

a. Which is more: 5 hundreds or 55 tens? _____

b. Which is less: 6 thousands or 61 hundreds? _____

c. What is the biggest number you can make with these digits: 2948? _____

d. What is the difference between: 98,430 and 97,430? _____

e. What do you need to add to 76,305 to make 76,605? _____

Write these numbers in figures.

a. Nine thousand, eight hundred and eight = _____

b. Eight thousand, six hundred and forty-two = _____

c. Three thousand, seven hundred and ninety-nine = _____

Work out the following:

a. 4590 ...+... 10 more is _____4600_____

b. 8934 .... 10 less is _____

c. 3193 .... 100 more is _____

d. 6176 .... 100 less is _____

e. 8321 .... 1000 more is _____

f. 5869 .... 1000 less is _____

Check out these numbers:

5000 five thousand

500   five hundred

50   fifty

5   five

0.5   nought point five

0.05 nought point nought five

Write these numbers in order from the smallest to the biggest.

Watch out for the decimals!

a. 5630, 521, 0.56, 5780, 540

_____ _____ _____ _____ _____

b. 6900, 0.06, 634, 691, 6999

_____ _____ _____ _____ _____

c. 0.70, 7809, 750, 0.07, 7001

_____ _____ _____ _____ _____

d. 8003, 0.83, 0.08, 855, 8300

_____ _____ _____ _____ _____

addition and subtraction

Add these numbers in your head:

$40 + 50 + 60 =$ _____

$20 + 70 + 10 =$ _____

$25 + 25 + 70 =$ _____

$50 + 25 + 30 =$ _____

When adding bigger numbers it is easier to use a written method.

For example:

Th	H	T	U
	1	8	6	7
+		2	3	5
	2	1	0	2
		1	1	1

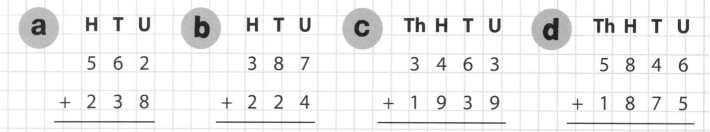

remember:

Add the units first. Carry over any tens to the tens column, hundreds to the hundreds column and thousands to the thousands column.

Add these numbers.

a

H	T	U
5	6	2
+ 2	3	8

b

H	T	U
3	8	7
+ 2	2	4

c

Th	H	T	U
3	4	6	3
+ 1	9	3	9

d

Th	H	T	U
5	8	4	6
+ 1	8	7	5

e Find the total of
$460 + 13 + 7 + 3402$

Th	H	T	U
+			

f Find the total of
$55 + 9 + 342 + 1348$

Th	H	T	U
+			

MAKE SURE THE NUMBERS ARE IN THE CORRECT COLUMNS.

Try these subtractions.

For example:

```
      Th   H    T    U
       0   13   11   1
       5    4    2    3
  –         7    6    5
  ─────────────────────
            6    5    8
```

remember:

Subtract the units first. Exchange (or borrow) from other columns if you need to, eg a ten for 10 units, a hundred for 10 tens and a thousand for 10 hundreds.

Subtract these numbers.

a

```
  H  T  U
  4  6  3
– 1  3  9
─────────

```

b

```
  H  T  U
  2  3  5
– 1  4  9
─────────

```

c

```
Th  H  T  U
 2  3  6  4
– 1  8  5  7
───────────

```

d

```
Th  H  T  U
 4  5  2  1
– 1  8  7  5
───────────

```

e

```
Th  H  T  U
 3  7  6  5
– 1  9  7  5
───────────

```

f

```
Th  H  T  U
 5  3  4  2
– 1  6  9  5
───────────

```

decimals

A **decimal** is part of a whole number. It is similar to a fraction.

0.5 is the same as ½

1.5 is the same as 1½

We say:

0.5 = nought point five

1.5 = one point five

remember:
The number before the decimal point is a whole number. The number after the decimal point is a part of a whole number.

Write these decimals on the number line.

0.2   0.5   1.3   1.5   1.9   0.7   1.1   0.8

0   1   2

Write these numbers in order from the smallest to the biggest.

a. 7.3, 6.5, 9.2, 5.1

_____ _____ _____ _____

b. 96p, £1.06, £96, £1.96

_____ _____ _____ _____

MONEY IS WRITTEN IN DECIMALS – SO IT'S WORTH YOUR WHILE GETTING TO KNOW THEM!

c. 0.5 cm, 1.5 cm, 2.5 cm, 1.2 cm

_____ _____ _____ _____

d. 5.2 m, 5.5 m, 5.1 m, 5.9 m

_____ _____ _____ _____

Money and other measures, such as length, weight and volume, use decimals.

For example:

100 cm = 1 m

150 cm = 1.5 m

1000 g = 1 kg

1100 g = 1.1 kg

1000 ml = 1 litre

1900 ml = 1.9 litres

Find out:

a. How many pence in £2.50? _____ p

b. What is 673p in pounds and pence? £ _____

c. How many centimetres in 1.10 metres? _____ cm

d. What is 350 cm written in metres? _____ m

e. What comes next? 5.0, 5.2, 5.4, _____ , _____

f. What comes next? 7.1, 6.9, 6.7, _____ , _____

g. What is 1400 g in kilograms? _____ kg

h. How many millilitres in 1.4 litres? _____ ml

Decimals have fraction equivalents.

For example:

$0.50 = \dfrac{1}{2}$ $0.25 = \dfrac{1}{4}$ $0.20 = \dfrac{1}{5}$ $0.1 = \dfrac{1}{10}$ $0.01 = \dfrac{1}{100}$

PUT THESE FRACTIONS IN A CALCULATOR TO CHECK THE DECIMAL EQUIVALENTS.

remember:

0.50 is the same as 0.5

In money, 0.5 would be worth 50p.

0.05 would be 5p.

Draw a line to join each decimal to its fraction equivalent.

| 0.20 | 0.02 | 0.60 | 0.75 | 0.35 | 0.10 |

| $\dfrac{75}{100}$ | $\dfrac{35}{100}$ | $\dfrac{20}{100}$ | $\dfrac{2}{100}$ | $\dfrac{10}{100}$ | $\dfrac{60}{100}$ |

x and ÷ 10 and 100

Look for the pattern when you multiply by 10:

5 x 10 = 50

50 x 10 = 500

500 x 10 = 5000

Look for the pattern when you divide by 10:

50 ÷ 10 = 5

500 ÷ 10 = 50

5000 ÷ 10 = 500

Find out:

a. What is 6 x 10? _____

b. What is 15 x 10? _____

c. What is 330 x 10? _____

d. What is 70 ÷10? _____

e. What is 200 ÷ 10? _____

f. What is 4000 ÷ 10? _____

Solve these problems.

a. Each packet contains 10 biscuits. There are 15 packets in a carton. How many biscuits are in the carton?

_____ biscuits

b. Dog food costs 80p per tin. Dig wants to buy 10 tins. How much money does he need?

£_____

c. A basic dog collar costs £3. A diamante dog collar costs ten times as much. How much is the diamante dog collar?

£_____

d. If a dog drinks 1.5 litres of water a day, how much will 10 dogs drink?

_____ litres

remember:

1.5 litres is 1500 millilitres.

Look for the pattern when you multiply by 100:

5 x 100 = 500

50 x 100 = 5000

500 x 100 = 50,000

Look for the pattern when you divide by 100:

500 ÷ 100 = 5

5000 ÷ 100 = 50

50,000 ÷ 100 = 500

Find out:

a. What is 3 x 100? _____

b. What is 25 x 100? _____

c. What is 410 x 100? _____

d. What is 200 ÷ 100? _____

e. What is 1000 ÷ 100? _____

f. What is 2000 ÷ 100? _____

Calculate the following:

a. One-tenth of 120 is _____

b. One-hundredth of 700 is _____

c. Two-tenths of 60 is _____

d. Two-hundredths of 800 is _____

e. Five-tenths (or ½) of £1.50 is _____

f. Five-hundredths of £1 is _____

WHICH WOULD YOU PREFER? ONE-HUNDREDTH OF £100 OR FIVE-TENTHS OF £20?

remember:

To find **one-tenth (⅒)** of something we **divide by 10**. To find **one-hundredth (¹⁄₁₀₀)** of something we **divide by 100**.

stick a reward sticker here!

9

number sequences

Count in 3s to 30

_____

Count in 6s to 60

_____

Count in 9s to 90

_____

WHAT DO YOU NOTICE ABOUT THE 3s, 6s AND 9s SEQUENCES?

Count in 2s to 20

_____

Count in 4s to 40

_____

Count in 8s to 80

_____

WHAT DO YOU NOTICE ABOUT THE 2s, 4s AND 8s SEQUENCES?

Count in 5s to 50

_____

Count in 10s to 100

_____

WHAT DO YOU NOTICE ABOUT THE 5s AND 10s SEQUENCES?

Count in 25s to 250

_____

Count in 50s to 500

_____

WHAT DO YOU NOTICE ABOUT THE 25s AND 50s SEQUENCES?

Count on from 11 in 5s

_____

Count back from 53 in 5s

_____

Count on from 10 in 9s

_____

Count back from 88 in 9s

_____

Complete this multiplication square. Then colour in the multiples of 3. What do you notice?

1	2	3	4	5	6	7	8	9	10
2	4	6	8	10		14	16		
3	6		12		18	21		27	
4		12	16	20		28	32	36	40
5		15	20					45	50
6				30	36	42	48		
7		21						63	70
8	16			40	48	56			
9	18	27	36	45	54		72	81	90
10	20	30	40	50	60	70	80	90	

remember:
Subtracting 9 is easier if you subtract 10 first, then add 1.

Complete this multiplication square. Then colour in the multiples of 4. What do you notice?

1	2	3	4	5	6	7	8	9	10
2		6	8	10		14			
3	6		12			21	24	27	
4	8							36	40
5		15	20	25	30		40		
6			24					54	60
7	14			35	42	49	56		
8					48		64	72	80
9	18	27	36	45					90
10	20	30	40			70	80	90	

fractions

A **fraction** is a part of a whole.

If we halve something, we divide it into two equal parts.

We write this as: $\frac{1}{2}$

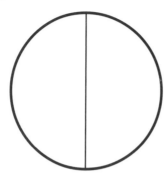

remember:

The number on top (called the **numerator**) represents the whole thing.

The number underneath (called the **denominator**) represents the number of parts.

Colour these fractions of the shapes.

1 Colour $\frac{1}{2}$

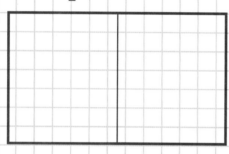

2 Colour $\frac{2}{3}$

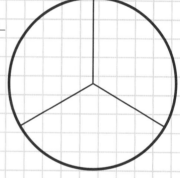

3 Colour $\frac{2}{4}$

4 Colour $\frac{4}{5}$

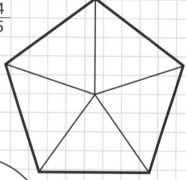

5 Colour $\frac{3}{6}$

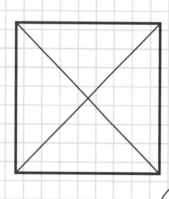

$\frac{2}{4}$ AND $\frac{3}{6}$ ARE THE SAME AS $\frac{1}{2}$!!

Fractions that have the same value are called **equivalent fractions**.

For example:

$\frac{1}{2}$ is the same as $\frac{4}{8}$, $\frac{5}{10}$, $\frac{6}{12}$ and $\frac{50}{100}$ etc.

Can you think of any other equivalent fractions? Write them in the space below.

Draw a ring around the fractions that are less than $\frac{1}{2}$.

$\frac{6}{14}$ $\frac{3}{8}$ $\frac{5}{10}$ $\frac{9}{20}$ $\frac{60}{100}$ $\frac{7}{16}$ $\frac{9}{12}$

Draw a ring around the fractions that are more than $\frac{1}{2}$.

$\frac{12}{20}$ $\frac{7}{12}$ $\frac{4}{8}$ $\frac{9}{16}$ $\frac{6}{18}$ $\frac{6}{10}$ $\frac{8}{24}$

Write these fractions in order from the smallest.

$\frac{1}{5}$ $\frac{3}{4}$ $\frac{1}{10}$ $\frac{3}{6}$

___   ___   ___   ___

remember:

You can simplify a fraction by dividing the top number and the bottom number by the same factor.

eg $\frac{12}{16}$ ($\div$ by 4) $= \frac{3}{4}$

What fraction of this shape is coloured?

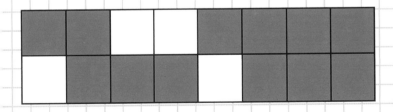

stick a
reward
sticker
here!

13

shapes

Name these shapes.

a

_____

b
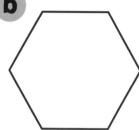

_____

c
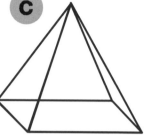

_____

d
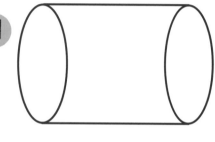

_____

e
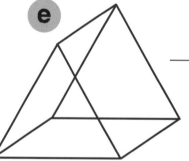

_____

Complete the following statement.

A cube has:

_____ faces.

_____ edges.

_____ corners (vertices).

edge

corner

face

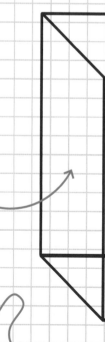

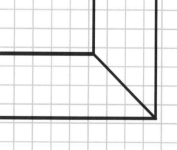

face

Write true (T) or false (F) next to each of these statements.

1. A triangle has 3 sides. ☐

2. A cuboid has 8 faces. ☐

3. A cylinder has 1 face. ☐

4. A cylinder has 2 edges. ☐

5. A triangular prism has 9 edges. ☐

6. A square has 4 equal sides. ☐

7. A pentagon has 6 sides. ☐

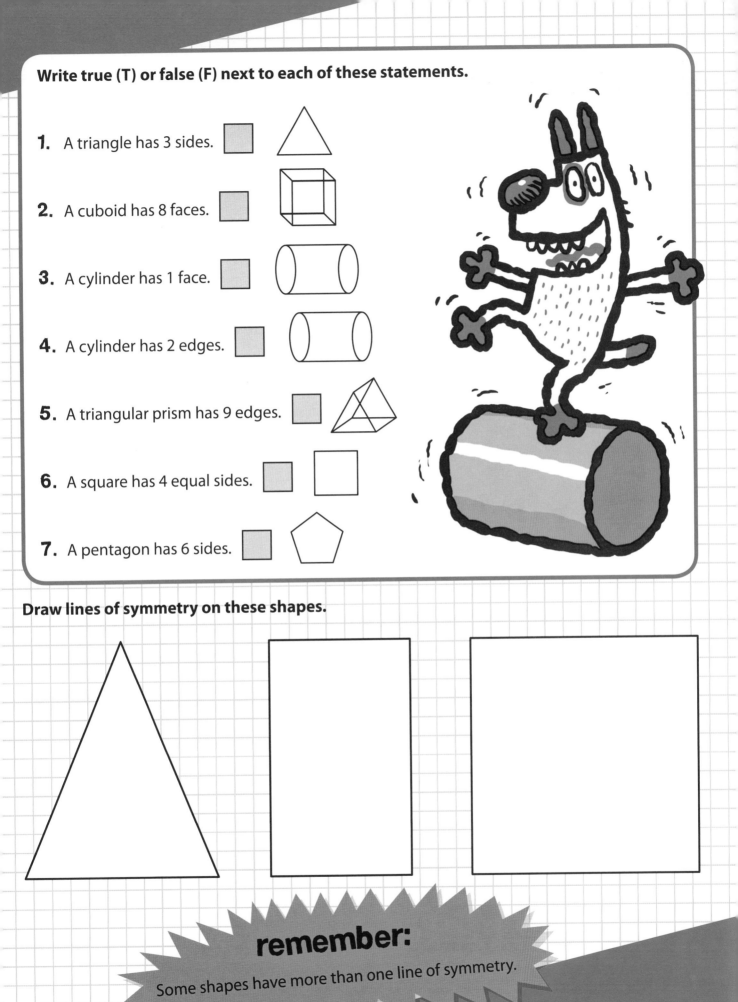

Draw lines of symmetry on these shapes.

remember:
Some shapes have more than one line of symmetry.

angles

An **angle** is a rotation around a point. We measure angles in **degrees** using a protractor.

remember:

The sign for 'more than' is > and 'less than' is <.

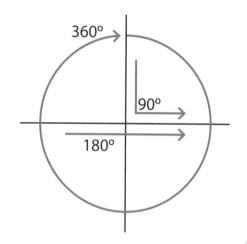

360 degrees = a circle

180 degrees = a straight line

90 degrees = a quarter-turn (a right angle)

An angle **less** than 90 degrees is called **acute**.

An angle **more** than 90 degrees is called **obtuse**.

Label these angles 'acute' or 'obtuse'.

a _____

b _____

c _____

d _____

Calculate the unknown angle.

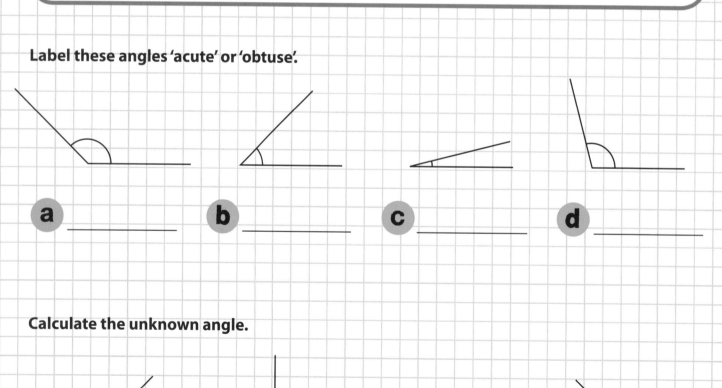

? 45°

? 90°

? 30°

135° ?

a _____

b _____

c _____

d _____

wow!

oops!

fab!

oh, no!

cool!

easy peasy!

nooo!

yes!!

woo!

oops!

wow!

yay!

brill!

lol

score!

woo!

yay!

yikes!

ok!

gr8!

yippee!

not bad!

great!

wicked!

cool!

ok!

brill!

fab!

cool!
ok!
brill!
fab!
yippee!
not bad!
great!
wicked!
yay!
yikes!
ok!
gr8!
wow!
oops!
fab!
oh, no!
cool!
easy peasy!
nooo!
yes!!
woo!
oops!
wow!
yay!
brill!
lol
score!
woo!

The angles in a triangle add up to 180 degrees.

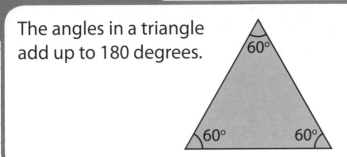

60°
60°   60°

remember:

If you know two of the angles in a triangle you can calculate the third angle by subtracting from 180.

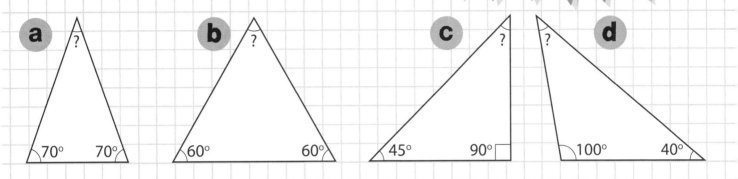

a
?
70°   70°
_____

b
?
60°   60°
_____

c
?
45°   90°
_____

d
?
100°   40°
_____

There are different types of triangle:

equilateral – 3 equal sides, 3 equal angles

isosceles – 2 equal sides, 2 equal angles

scalene – no equal sides, no equal angles

right-angled – one right angle

Identify these triangles using the definitions above.

a
_____

b
_____

c
_____

d
_____

remember:

A right-angle triangle is labelled like this:

stick a reward sticker here!

17

multiplication

Multiply the numbers below using the following method.

For example: 56 x 7 = (50 x 7) + (6 x 7)

= 350 + 42

= **392**

Now it's your turn!

a 43 x 5 = (_____) + (_____)

= _____ + _____

= _____

b 28 x 3 = (_____) + (_____)

= _____ + _____

= _____

c 36 x 4 = (_____) + (_____)

= _____ + _____

= _____

d 69 x 10 = (_____) + (_____)

= _____ + _____

= _____

Multiply the numbers below using the grid method.

For example: **52 x 36**

X	50	2	Total
30	1500	60	= 1560
6	300	12	= 312
			= **1872**

Give it a go!

a 27 x 34

X			Total
			=
			=
			=

b 41 x 16

X			Total
			=
			=
			=

Find the answers to these long multiplications using the following methods.

For example:

```
      1 4 2
  x     2 6
  _____
  2 8 4 0  (x20)
      8 5 2  (x6)
  _____
  3 6 9 2
```

X	100	40	2	Total
20	2000	800	40	= 2840
6	600	240	12	= 852

= 3692

a

```
      2 3 5
  x     2 5
  _____
           (x20)

           (x5)
  _____
```

X				Total
				=
				=

=

b

```
      4 1 6
  x     2 7
  _____
           (x20)

           (x7)
  _____
```

X				Total
				=
				=

=

c

```
      3 0 8
  x     2 4
  _____
           (x20)

           (x4)
  _____
```

X				Total
				=
				=

=

d

```
      2 3 2
  x     3 2
  _____
           (x30)

           (x2)
  _____
```

X				Total
				=
				=

=

division

Division is the opposite of multiplication.

For example:

$7 \times 6 = 42$ **So...** $42 \div 7 = 6$ and $42 \div 6 = 7$

Write two division facts for each multiplication below.

a. $8 \times 10 =$ _____

b. $80 \times 10 =$ _____

_____

_____

_____

_____

c. $50 \times 5 =$ _____

d. $500 \times 5 =$ _____

_____

_____

_____

_____

Dividing long numbers in your head is difficult so you need to learn a written method.

For example:

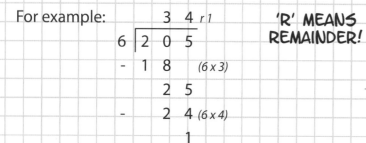

```
        3  4 r 1
   6 | 2  0  5
   -  1  8      (6 x 3)
         2  5
   -     2  4   (6 x 4)
            1
```

'R' MEANS REMAINDER!

remember:

Division is also like repeated subtraction.

E.g. $42 \div 6 = 42 - 6 - 6 - 6 - 6 - 6 - 6 - 6$

a **b** **c** **d** **e**

```
5 | 4  5  7
```

```
3 | 6  0  4
```

```
2 | 1  5  6
```

```
8 | 3  4  7
```

```
4 | 5  2  0
```

Always try to estimate your answers first when you are dividing.

For example: **300 ÷ 9**

You know that 300 ÷ 10 = 30 so you can estimate that 300 ÷ 9 will be a bit more than 30.

Now do the division to find out the answer …

```
           3  3 r3
      9 │ 3  0  0
        -  2  7     (3 x 9)
              3  0
        -        2  7  (3 x 9)
                    3
```

Work out these division problems.

Estimate your answers first.

1. Share £11.50 equally between Dig and Kit.

2. 720 divide by 3.

3. How many 150 cm dog leads can you make from 600 cm?

4. 696 ÷ 6

5. Share 2060 by 20.

6. How many groups of 8 are there in 448?

Do your working out here...

Rounding numbers

When making rough estimates in your head, rounding numbers (up or down) is useful.

For example, numbers from 101 to 104 can be rounded down to 100 and from 105 to 109 rounded up to 110.

Round these numbers to the nearest ten.

a. 21 _____

b. 687 _____

c. 453 _____

d. 999 _____

area and perimeter

Area is a measurement of the space inside a shape.

If each square represents 1 square cm, what area is shaded?

_____ cm²

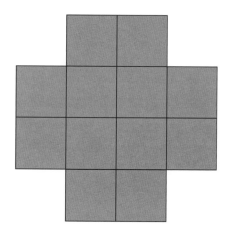

Perimeter is the distance around the edges of a shape.

What is the perimeter of the shape above? _____ cm

Draw your own shape in this space and find out its perimeter and area.

Find the area and perimeter of these shapes.

For example:

6 cm

2 cm

area = 2 x 6 = 12 cm²

perimeter = 2 + 2 + 6 + 6 = 16 cm

a

14 cm

10 cm

area = _____ cm²

perimeter = _____ cm

b

20 cm

4 cm

area = _____ cm²

perimeter = _____ cm

c

15 cm

7 cm

area = _____ cm²

perimeter = _____ cm

d

10 cm

30 cm

area = _____ cm²

perimeter = _____ cm

What is the approximate area of this rectangle?

Round the decimals down or up to find out.

12.4 cm

19.7 cm

area = _____ cm²

23

coordinates

Coordinates are the numbers we use to pinpoint a place on a graph or map.

Look at the map below. You will find Skull Rock at (4, 5). Write the coordinates for the following:

a. Creepy cave (__ , __)

b. Stinky swamp (__ , __)

c. Skull and crossbones (__ , __)

d. Buried treasure (__ , __)

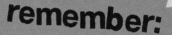

remember:
First you read along the x axis, then the y axis.

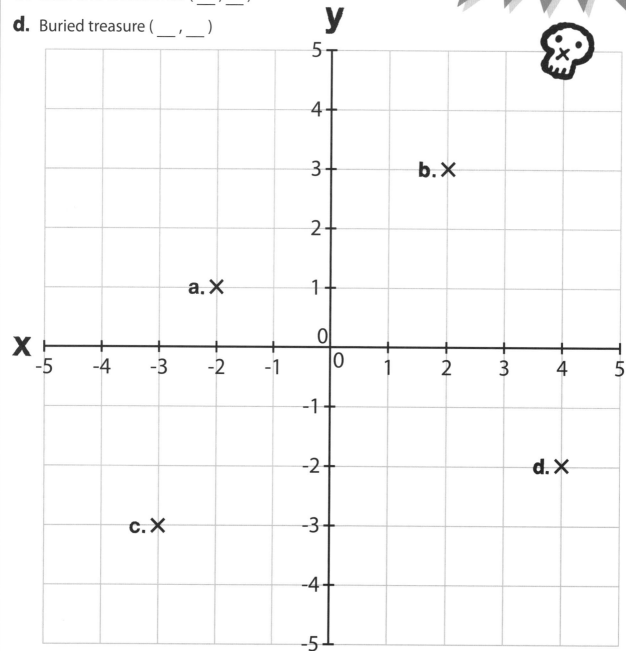

Draw your own treasure map with buried treasure.

Write the coordinates of the buried treasure here: (__ , __)

Write the coordinates for three other important places on your map.

Place name: _____ (__ , __)

Place name: _____ (__ , __)

Place name: _____ (__ , __)

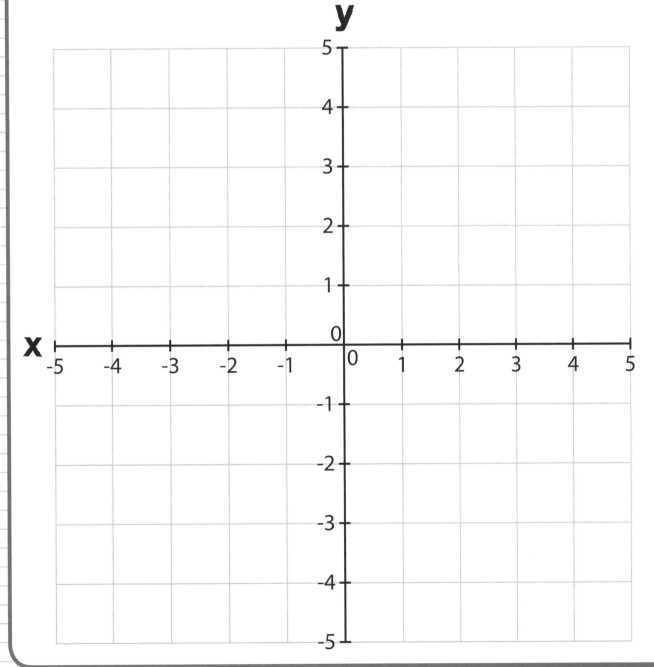

negative numbers

Complete this temperature scale.

(-)(-9)(-)(-)(-6)(-5)(-4)(-)(-2)(-1)(0)(1)(2)(3)(4)(5)(6)(7)(8)(9)(10)

Use the number line to do these subtractions by counting back.

a. - 4 – 6 = _____

b. - 3 – 5 = _____

c. -1 – 4 = _____

d. 6 – 8 = _____

e. 2 – 5 = _____

stick a reward sticker here!

remember:

- 4 – 3 = - 7

But 4 – 3 = 1

BRRR! IT'S FREEZING IN HERE.

YOU ARE SO NEGATIVE!

percentages

A **percentage** is a part of a hundred.

Revise these percentage and fraction equivalents:

$1\% = \frac{1}{100}$ (one hundredth)

$10\% = \frac{10}{100}$ (one-tenth)

$25\% = \frac{25}{100}$ (one quarter)

$50\% = \frac{50}{100}$ (half)

What percentage of each shape is shaded?

 a

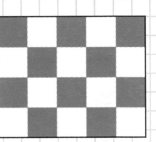

b

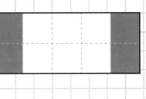

Now try these!

a. 50% of 100 = _____

b. 50% of 40 = _____

c. 25% of £1 = _____p

d. 10% of £1 = _____p

e. 10% of 50p = _____p

f. $\frac{1}{4}$ of 80 cm = _____cm

g. 25% of 1 kg = _____g

h. $\frac{1}{10}$ of 30 ml = _____ml

Colour in 75% of each shape.

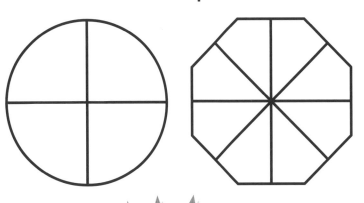

remember:

$75\% = 50\% + 25\%$ or $\frac{1}{2} + \frac{1}{4}$

27

graphs

Look at the bar graph that shows the height of children in Class 6.

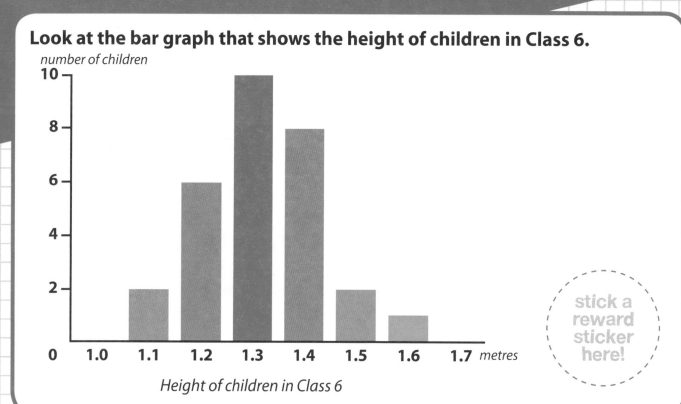

Height of children in Class 6

stick a reward sticker here!

Answer the following questions based on the graph.

a. What height are most children in Class 6? _____m

b. What is 1.2 m in centimetres? _____cm

c. What height are the shortest children in the class? _____cm

d. What is the difference in height between the shortest and the tallest child? _____cm

e. How many children are in Class 6? _____ children

WHO'S TALLER?

Look at the pie chart that shows the children's eye colours in Class 7.

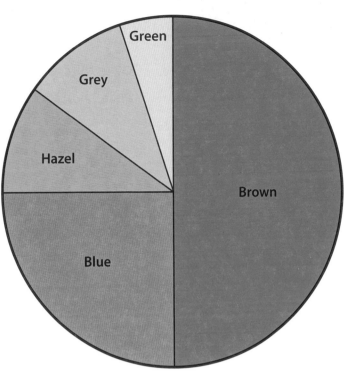

Green

Grey

Hazel

Brown

Blue

Eye colour of children in Class 7

There are 20 children in Class 7.

Answer the following questions based on the pie chart.

a. Which is the most common eye colour? _____

b. Which is the least common eye colour? _____

c. How many children have grey eyes? _____

d. What percentage of children have brown eyes? _____%

e. What percentage of children have blue eyes? _____%

LOOK INTO MY EYES!

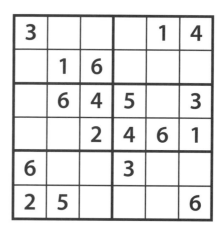

1. Count all the squares you can find in this shape.

2. Complete this number sudoku so that each 3 x 2 block includes all the numbers from 1 to 6. The columns and rows must also include all these numbers.

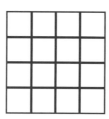

3				1	4
	1	6			
	6	4	5		3
		2	4	6	1
6			3		
2	5				6

3. Complete these multiplication tables.

X	7	4	2	Total
3	21			= 39
	42			=
		32		=
5				=

X	6		9	Total
	36			=
7		70		=
			27	=
	30			=

4. Write the factors for each number on these spider diagrams.

a
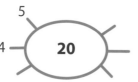
5
4 — 20

b
24

c
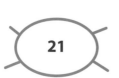
21

d
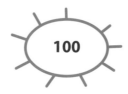
100

remember:

A **factor** is a number that will divide evenly (without a remainder) into another number, eg 3, 9 and 1 are factors of 9.

5. A short dog lead is 100 cm long. A long lead is 2 m. How much longer is the long lead in centimetres? _____ cm

answers

number values

a. 4098 = 4000 + 0 + 90 + 8
b. 5667 = 5000 + 600 + 60 + 7
c. 3824 = 3000 + 800 + 20 + 4
d. 1951 = 1000 + 900 + 50 + 1

a. 55 tens is more
b. 6 thousands is less
c. 9842
d. 1000
e. 300

a. 9808
b. 8642
c. 3799

a. 4590 + 10 = 4600
b. 8934 − 10 = 8924
c. 3193 + 100 = 3293
d. 6176 − 100 = 6076
e. 8321 + 1000 = 9321
f. 5869 − 1000 = 4869

a. 0.56, 521, 540, 5630, 5780
b. 0.06, 634, 691, 6900, 6999
c. 0.07, 0.70, 750, 7001, 7809
d. 0.08, 0.83, 855, 8003, 8300

addition and subtraction

40 + 50 + 60 = 150
20 + 70 + 10 = 100
25 + 25 + 70 = 120
50 + 25 + 30 = 105

a. 800   **a.** 324
b. 611   **b.** 86
c. 5402   **c.** 507
d. 7721   **d.** 2646
e. 3882   **e.** 1790
f. 1754   **f.** 3647

decimals

	0.2		0.5	0.7 0.8		1.1	1.3	1.5		1.9	
0					1					2

a. 5.1, 6.5, 7.3, 9.2
b. 96p, £1.06, £1.96, £96
c. 0.5 cm, 1.2 cm, 1.5 cm, 2.5 cm
d. 5.1 m, 5.2 m, 5.5 m, 5.9 m

a. 250p
b. £6.73
c. 110 cm
d. 3.5 m
e. 5.0, 5.2, 5.4, 5.6, 5.8
f. 7.1, 6.9, 6.7, 6.5, 6.3
g. 1.4 kg
h. 1400 ml

0.20 = 20/100
0.02 = 2/100
0.60 = 60/100
0.75 = 75/100

0.35 = 35/100
0.10 = 10/100

x and ÷ 10 and 100

a. 60
b. 150
c. 3300
d. 7
e. 20
f. 400

a. 150 biscuits
b. £8
c. £30
d. 15 litres

a. 300
b. 2500
c. 41 000
d. 2
e. 10
f. 20

a. One-tenth of 120 is 12
b. One-hundredth of 700 is 7
c. Two-tenths of 60 is 12
d. Two-hundredths of 800 is 16
e. Five-tenths (or ½) of £1.50 is 75p
f. Five-hundredths of £1 is 5p

number sequences

3s: 3, 6, 9, 12, 15, 18, 21, 24, 27, 30
6s: 6, 12, 18, 24, 30, 36, 42, 48, 54, 60
9s: 9, 18, 27, 36, 45, 54, 63, 72, 81, 90

The 3s sequence is double the 6s.
The 9s sequence is the 6s plus the 3s.

2s: 2, 4, 6, 8, 10, 12, 14, 16, 18, 20
4s: 4, 8, 12, 16, 20, 24, 28, 32, 36, 40
8s: 8, 16, 24, 32, 40, 48, 56, 64, 72, 80

The 4s sequence is double the 2s.
The 8s sequence is the 4s plus the 2s.

5s: 5, 10, 15, 20, 25, 30, 35, 40, 45, 50
10s: 10, 20, 30, 40, 50, 60, 70, 80, 90, 100

The 10s sequence is double the 5s.

25s: 25, 50, 75, 100, 125, 150, 175, 200, 225, 250
50s: 50, 100, 150, 200, 250, 300, 350, 400, 450, 500

The 50s sequence is double the 25s.

11, 16, 21, 26, 31, 36, 41, 46, 51 and so on...
53, 48, 43, 38, 33, 28, 23, 18, 13, 8, 3
10, 19, 28, 37, 46, 55, 64, 73, 82, 91 and so on...
88, 79, 70, 61, 52, 43, 34, 25, 16, 7

Multiples of 3

1	2	3	4	5	6	7	8	9	10
2	4	6	8	10	12	14	16	18	20
3	6	9	12	15	18	21	24	27	30
4	8	12	16	20	24	28	32	36	40
5	10	15	20	25	30	35	40	45	50
6	12	18	24	30	36	42	48	54	60
7	14	21	28	35	42	49	56	63	70
8	16	24	32	40	48	56	64	72	80
9	18	27	36	45	54	63	72	81	90
10	20	30	40	50	60	70	80	90	100

Multiples of 4

1	2	3	4	5	6	7	8	9	10
2	4	6	8	10	12	14	16	18	20
3	6	9	12	15	18	21	24	27	30
4	8	12	16	20	24	28	32	36	40
5	10	15	20	25	30	35	40	45	50
6	12	18	24	30	36	42	48	54	60
7	14	21	28	35	42	49	56	63	70
8	16	24	32	40	48	56	64	72	80
9	18	27	36	45	54	63	72	81	90
10	20	30	40	50	60	70	80	90	100

fractions

1.

2.

3.

4.

5.

These fractions are less than ½:
⁶⁄₁₄   ³⁄₈   ⁹⁄₂₀   ⁷⁄₁₆

These fractions are more than ½:
¹²⁄₂₀   ⁷⁄₁₂   ⁹⁄₁₆   ⁶⁄₁₀

These fractions are in order from the smallest: $\frac{1}{10}$ $\frac{1}{3}$ $\frac{3}{6}$ $\frac{3}{4}$

$\frac{12}{16}$ (or $\frac{6}{8}$ or $\frac{3}{4}$) of the shape is coloured.

shapes
a. rectangle
b. (regular) hexagon
c. square-based pyramid
d. cylinder
e. (triangular) prism

A cube has:
6 faces
12 edges
8 corners (vertices)

1. True: a triangle has 3 sides.
2. False: because a cuboid has 6 faces.
3. False: because a cylinder has 3 faces.
4. True: a cylinder has 2 edges.
5. True: a triangular prism has 9 edges.
6. True: a square has 4 equal sides
7. False: because a pentagon has 5 sides.

angles
a. obtuse
b. acute
c. acute
d. obtuse

a. 135°
b. 90°
c. 150°
d. 45°

a. 40°
b. 60°
c. 45°
d. 40°

a. isosceles
b. scalene
c. right-angled
d. equilateral

multiplication
a. 43 x 5 = (40 x 5) + (3 x 5)
= 200 + 15
= 215

b. 28 x 3 = (20 x 3) + (8 x 3)
= 60 + 24
= 84

c. 36 x 4 = (30 x 4) + (6 x 4)
= 120 + 24
= 144

d. 69 x 10 = (60 x10) + (9 x10)
= 600 + 90
= 690

a. 27 x 34

X	20	7	Total
30	600	210	= 810
4	80	28	= 108
			= 918

b. 41 x 16

X	40	1	Total
10	400	10	= 410
6	240	6	= 246
			= 656

a.
```
    2 3 5
x     2 5
4 7 0 0 (x20)
1 1 7 5 (x5)
5 8 7 5
```

X	200	30	5	Total
20	4000	600	100	=4700
5	1000	150	25	=1175
				=5875

b.
```
    4 1 6
x     2 7
8 3 2 0 (x20)
2 9 1 2 (x7)
1 1 2 3 2
```

X	400	10	6	Total
20	8000	200	120	=8320
7	2800	70	42	=2912
				=11232

c.
```
    3 0 8
x     2 4
6 1 6 0 (x20)
1 2 3 2 (x4)
7 3 9 2
```

X	300	0	8	Total
20	6000	0	160	=6160
4	1200	0	32	=1232
				=7392

d.
```
    2 3 2
x     3 2
6 9 6 0 (x30)
  4 6 4 (x2)
7 4 2 4
```

X	200	30	2	Total
30	6000	900	60	=6960
2	400	60	4	= 464
				=7424

division
a. 8 x 10 = 80
80 ÷ 10 = 8
80 ÷ 8 = 10

b. 80 x 10 = 800
800 ÷ 10 = 80
800 ÷ 80 = 10

c. 50 x 5 = 250
250 ÷ 5 = 50
250 ÷ 50 = 5

d. 500 x 5 = 2500
2500 ÷ 5 = 500
2500 ÷ 500 = 5

a. 91 r 2
c. 78
e. 130

b. 201 r 1
d. 43 r 3

1. £5.75
3. 4 leads
5. 103

2. 240
4. 116
6. 56 groups

Rounding numbers
a. 20
c. 450

b. 690
d. 1000

area and perimeter
The area of the shape is 12 cm².
The perimeter of the shape is 16 cm.

a. area = 140 cm²   perimeter = 48 cm
b. area = 80 cm²   perimeter = 48 cm
c. area = 105 cm²   perimeter = 44 cm
d. area = 300 cm²   perimeter = 80 cm

The area of the rectangle is approximately
12 x 20 cm = 240 cm²

coordinates
a. (-2, 1)   **b.** (2, 3)
c. (-3 , -3)   **d.** (4, -2)

negative numbers
a. - 4 – 6 = -10
b. - 3 – 5 = -8
c. -1 – 4 = -5
d. 6 – 8 = -2
e. 2 – 5 = -3

percentages
a. $\frac{10}{20}$ or $\frac{1}{2}$ or 50%
b. $\frac{4}{10}$ or $\frac{2}{5}$ or 40%

a. 50% of 100 = 50
b. 50% of 40 = 20
c. 25% of £1 = 25p
d. 10% of £1 = 10p
e. 10% of 50p = 5p
f. ¼ of 80 cm = 20 cm
g. 25% of 1 kg = 250 g
h. $\frac{1}{10}$ of 30 ml = 3 ml

graphs
a. 1.3 m
b. 120 cm
c. 110 cm
d. 50 cm
e. 29 children

a. brown
b. green
c. 2 children
d. 50%
e. 25%

puzzles
1. You should find at least 26 squares!

2.

3	2	5	6	1	4
4	1	6	2	3	5
1	6	4	5	2	3
5	3	2	4	6	1
6	4	1	3	5	2
2	5	3	1	4	6

3.

X	7	4	2	Total
3	21	12	6	= 39
6	42	24	12	= 78
8	56	32	16	= 104
5	35	20	10	= 65

X	6	10	9	Total
6	36	60	54	= 150
7	42	70	63	= 175
3	18	30	27	= 75
5	30	50	45	= 125

4. a. 20, 1, 10, 2, 5, 4
b. 24, 1, 6, 4, 8, 3, 2, 12
c. 21, 1, 7, 3
d. 100, 1, 10, 20, 5, 25, 4, 50, 2

5. 100 cm